Minds-On
FUN FOR WINTER

Enrichment Activities for Children in Grades K-4

By Judy Beach and Kathleen Spencer

Fearon Teacher Aids
Simon & Schuster Supplementary Education Group

Editors: Sue Mogard and Marilyn Trow
Copyeditor: Kristin Eclov
Design: Rose Sheifer
Illustration: Judy Beach
Cover Design: Marek/Janci Design

ISBN 0-86653-947-6

Printed in the United States of America

1.9 8 7 6 5 4 3 2

Challenge a child's imagination
And you've opened up a door.
But to keep that door from closing,
You must challenge them some more!

Contents

Using *Minds-On Fun for Winter*

Minds-On Fun for Winter is a special seasonal supplement designed to increase a young child's vocabulary and enrich your present curriculum. The activities motivate children to stretch their imaginations and practice their newly acquired skills in creative ways!

Each month, you can challenge your class with . . .

- **A calendar** filled with suggestions for fun days that children may enjoy both at home and at school.
- **Poems** that capture the light-heartedness of the season and enrich the children's sense of rhythm and rhyme.
- **A story (or play)** that promotes creative dramatic play.
- **Questioning strategies** that encourage critical-thinking skills in the areas of knowledge, comprehension, application, analysis, synthesis, and evaluation.
- **A rebus activity** that helps children discover more about context clues in a fun way.
- **Shape booklets** that offer a creative format for journal writings, spelling practice, writing communications to parents, and other writing experiences.
- **Story headers** that motivate children to freely and imaginatively express their ideas about various topics.
- **Creative-writing activities** on seasonal topics that encourage children to use their communication skills and imaginatively express themselves.
- **A gameboard** that may be used to encourage the growth of social skills and to review and reinforce skills presented in your classroom. For example, use the blank reproducible cards to review basic math facts and have the children move tokens along the gameboard the same number of spaces as the answers. Or review vowel sounds (c__t), assigning each vowel a specific number of moves (a = 2 moves, e = 3 moves, and so on).
- **Blank reproducibles** that may be used for calendar numbers, nametags, word cards, alphabet cards, and so on.
- **Certificates** for recording positive statements that motivate and excite the children and help them grow in self-confidence.
- **Reproducible notes** that are perfect for sending short messages home to parents or for writing reward notes to the children.
- **Reproducible art** designed to jazz up memos, notes, and bulletin boards (trace onto clear transparencies and use an overhead to project the images onto a bulletin board for tracing).

DECEMBER ACTIVITIES

December Activities

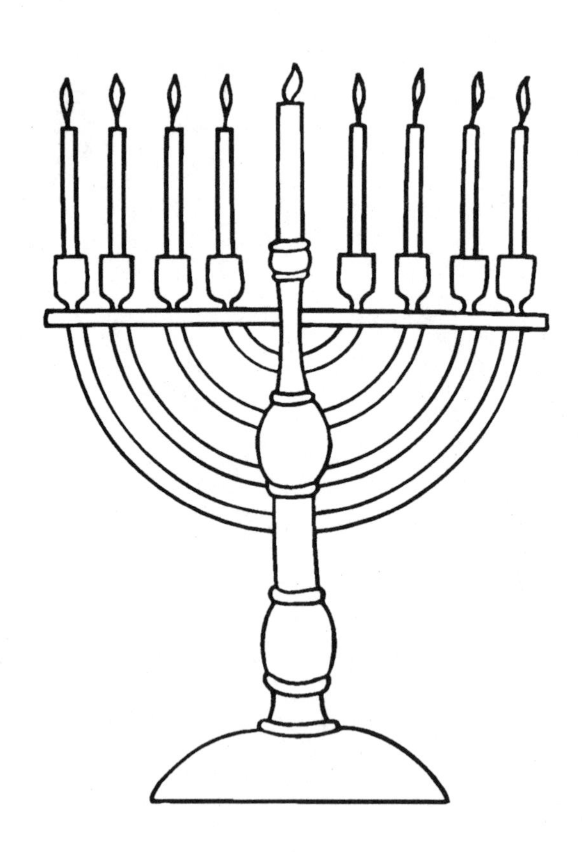

Name ______________________________

December

Sunday	Monday	Tuesday	Wednesday	Thursday	Friday	Saturday

CALENDAR ACTIVITIES

Print the following activities on squares of paper the same size as the spaces on the monthly calendar. Have the children cut out the following activity cards and then paste them on different calendar days.

Make a paper chain to count the days remaining until Christmas.

Make your Christmas list for Santa.

Make and decorate Christmas, Kwanzaa, and Hanukkah cookies. Don't forget to eat one! M-m-m.

Make a dreidel out of clay. Sing "I Have a Little Dreidel."

Make an extra-special Christmas card for your mom.

Santa's watching! Do something nice for a friend.

Ask your librarian to help you find information about Kwanzaa in the library.

Hang up your Christmas stocking.

Christmas Day

As the day turns into evening
And the world says its goodnights,
The streets are lit with colors
From strings of Christmas lights.

You can hear the carolers singing
As they pass along their way,
Singing songs of peace and joy
You'll find on Christmas Day.

Hanukkah: The Festival of Lights

Light the candles, shining bright
On the Hanukkah menorah
To celebrate the Maccabees fight.
Then let's dance the hora.

Light the candles one by one
For eight full days and nights.
Games are played and songs are sung
The Festival of Lights.

My Wish List

I made out my list for Santa last night.
Mom checked my spelling. She said it was right.
I printed each line the best that I could.
I even sent pictures. Mom said that I should.
I asked for a bike and a boat with a sail,
But I really want a puppy with a wagging tail.

Bedtime

It's cold outside,
Can you hear the wind?
Little animals are scurrying.

You're home in bed
Safe and warm as a bear.
Go to sleep now, please, no hurrying.

Nibble's Christmas Surprise

Narrator: A candy cane fell off the Christmas tree
And a little gray mouse came across it while looking for cheese.
His name was Nibbles and he lived in the wall
With a few dozen cousins that lived down the hall.

All: Jingle! Jingle! Be careful, Nibbles!
Could that be the cat?

Narrator: Normally Nibbles was very fair.
Everything that he found, with his family he'd share.
But this candy cane was something he'd never had.
He'd eat just a little. That wasn't so bad.

All: Jingle! Jingle! Be careful, Nibbles!
Could that be the cat?

Narrator: But it tasted so good that he got carried away.
Soon nothing was left of that big candy cane.
You can just imagine how greedy he'd become.
Besides feeling sick, he just wanted his mom.

All: Jingle! Jingle! Be careful, Nibbles!
Could that be the cat?

Narrator: He heard the jingling of the bells on the cat.
He knew he should run, but he said, "I can't."
He had candy cane "goo" all over his hair.

All: Jingle! Jingle! Be careful, Nibbles!
Could that be the cat?

Narrator: He pulled and he tugged, but he couldn't get free.
Oh, no! Somehow his ear got stuck to his knee.
He was stuck to the floor, so there he sat.
He hoped that he wouldn't be seen by the cat.

All: Jingle! Jingle! Be careful, Nibbles!
Could that be the cat?

Narrator: Then down through the chimney came Santa's big pack.
It was followed by Santa.
Phew! It wasn't the cat!
It was only the bells on Santa's red hat.

All: Jingle! Jingle! Ho! Ho! Ho!
It wasn't the cat!

Narrator: Santa's eyes twinkled and he tried not to laugh
At this sticky fat mouse in a tangled mess.
How he got there was easy to see.
The candy cane wrapper was still stuck to his knee.

All: Jingle! Jingle!
Ho! Ho! Ho!

Narrator: Santa helped Nibbles get unstuck from the floor.
Nibbles said, "I'll never do that anymore!"
This lesson he learned, and he'd never forget,
Being greedy can lead you to things you'll regret.

All: Jingle! Jingle!
Ho! Ho! Ho!

Narrator: Santa sent Nibbles off to his bed
With a sack filled with goodies
To share with his friends.

QUESTIONS AND ACTIVITIES FOR THE STORY

1. What was Nibbles out searching for?
2. Who was Nibbles afraid he might meet?
3. Who rescued Nibbles?
4. Retell the story in your own words. Illustrate the story.
5. What is this story all about?
6. Nibbles was a greedy mouse. What are some examples of greed? Tell about a time when greed got you in trouble.
7. If you were Nibbles' parents, what might you say to him about his greedy behavior?
8. List five or more things that you could share with friends and family.
9. Design an invention Nibbles might use if he ever gets stuck again.
10. Suppose Santa never appeared. Write a new ending to this story.

Name ____

Cut out the pictures below and paste them in the correct boxes.

The [ ] was all loaded up and ready to go. The [ ] were lined up out in the [ ]. All the [ ] were packed in a very big [ ].

[ ] had to put on his furry, warm [ ]. At last they were ready. The little [ ] waved good-by. The reindeer took off with a wink of an [ ].

This booklet belongs to
(name)

This booklet belongs to
(name)

Name ______________________________

Name________________________________

It was the middle of December. The air was cool and. . . . Describe what happened.

Attach to the top portion of your story.

Attach to the bottom portion of your story.

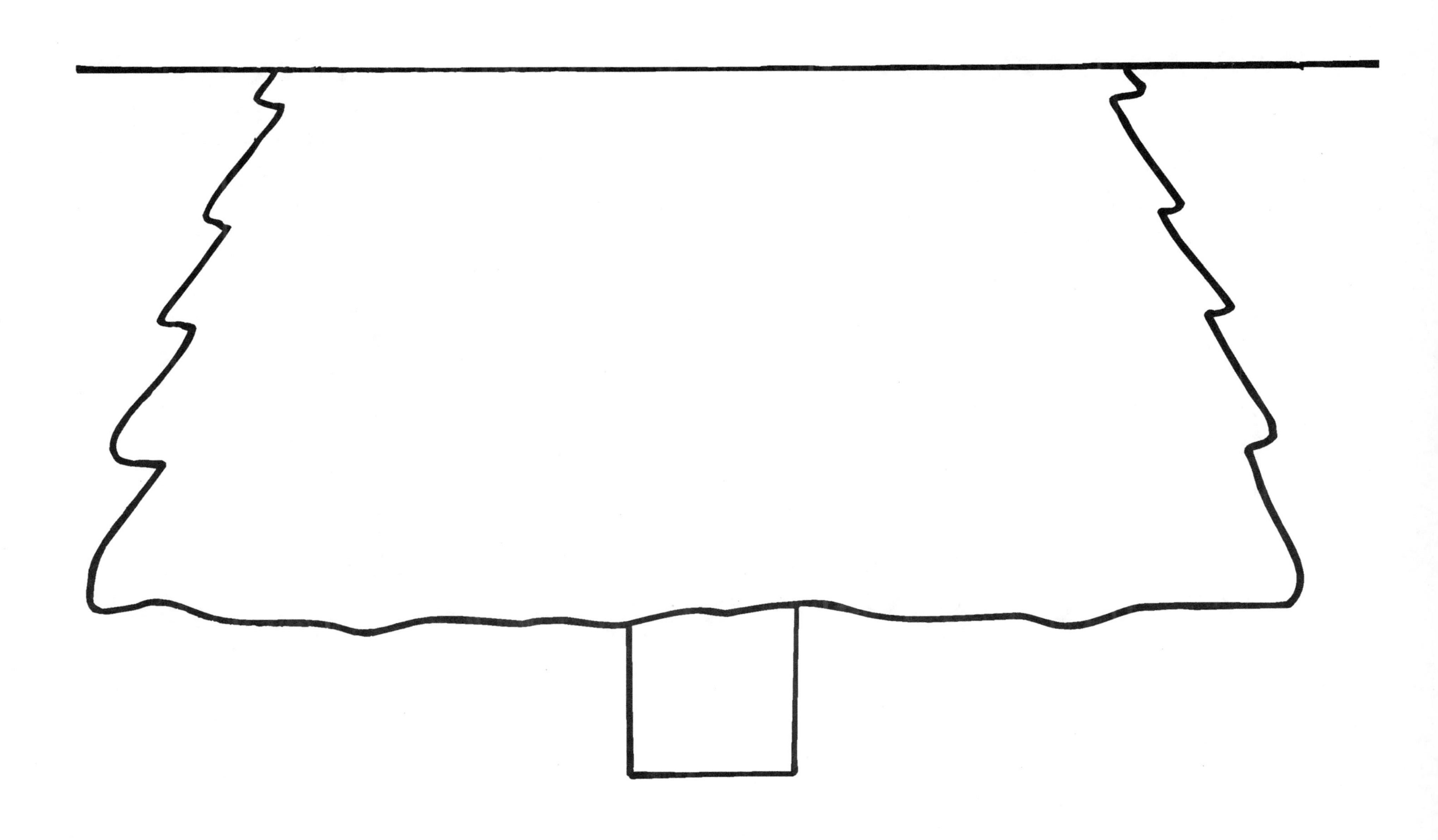

Name ________________________________

Make up a story,
Or maybe a song,
To celebrate Kwanzaa.
It needn't be long.

Attach to the top portion of your story or song.

Name ____________________

Ah-choo! Sniffle! Sniffle!
It sounds like Rudolph is catching a cold.

Ah-choo! Sniffle! Sniffle!
No telling what a cold could do to his shiny red nose.

Ah-ah-choo! Sniffle! Sniffle!
Rudolph's nose is running and his eyes are red.
His head is all stuffed up. He should be in bed.

Ah-ah-choo! Sniffle! Sniffle!
When Rudolph blew his nose, he blew out his shiny red light.
Now who will guide Santa and his reindeer tonight?

Name____

Write a letter to Santa Claus.
Mail it to the North Pole.

Name_______________________________________

To build this house, use your favorite treats. This is a house that you can eat!
On the house below, illustrate where your treats will go!

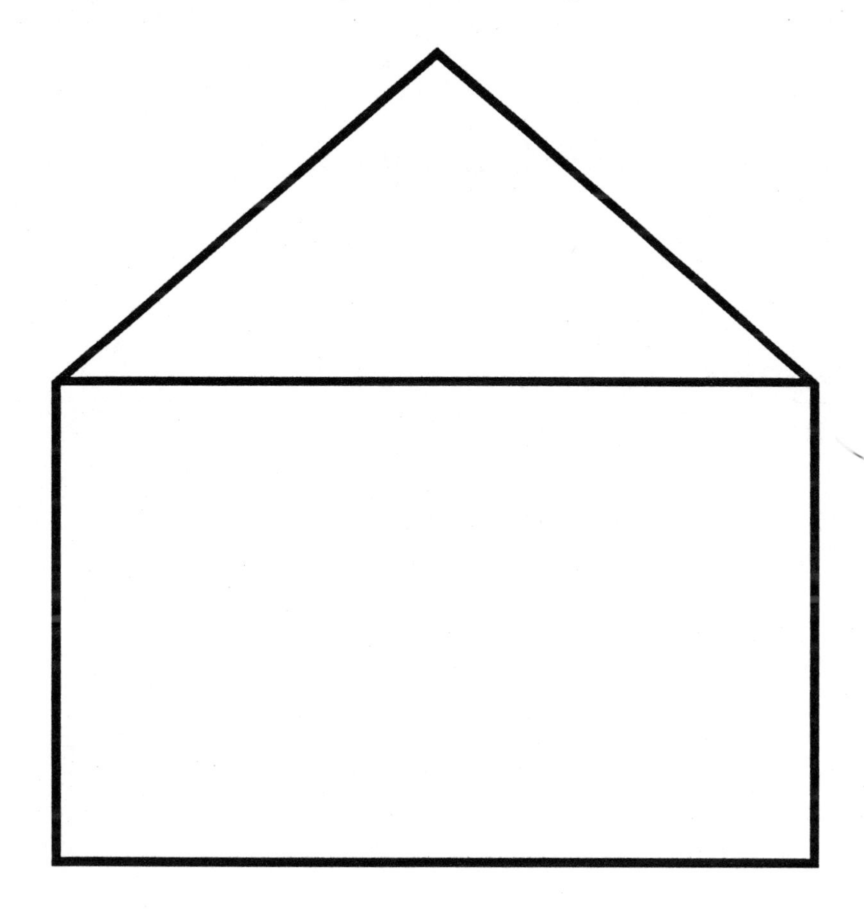

List all the treats you'll need to complete your house:

1. ____

2. ____

3. ____

4. ____

5. ____

Name ______________________________

Hanukkah lights, fruits and nuts, songs and dancing,
Bright candles, a menorah, and potato latkes.
The tastes, the smells, the things we hear and see
During the winter Festival of Lights.

What do you know or what can you find out about Hanukkah?

The "tastes" of Hanukkah

1. ______________________________

2. ______________________________

The "smells" of Hanukkah

1. ______________________________

2. ______________________________

The "sounds" of Hanukkah

1. ______________________________

2. ______________________________

The "sights" of Hanukkah

1. ______________________________

2. ______________________________

Name ______________________________

The elves found Santa's suit on a hook.
It hadn't been cleaned and it was covered with soot.
Mrs. Claus was busy doing her last-minute baking,
So she asked the elves to help her out.

Oh! Oh! In went the steaming hot water
And out came a crumpled red suit.
Oh! Oh! Into a steamy hot dryer it went
And out came a shrunken red suit.

Proud as can be, the elves gave the clean suit to Santa.
But when Santa put it on, it didn't fit!
The pants came up to the top of his knees
And the jacket would rip with one little sneeze.

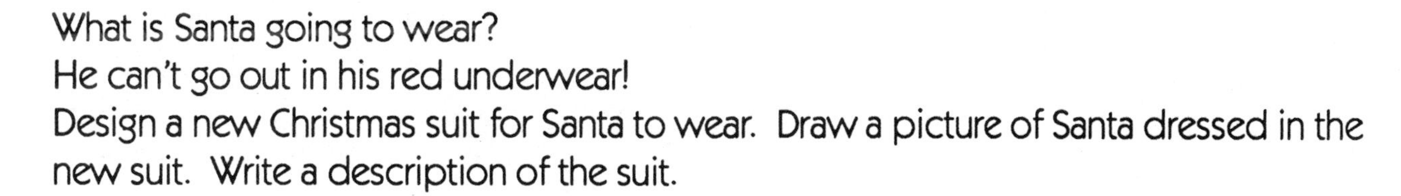

What is Santa going to wear?
He can't go out in his red underwear!
Design a new Christmas suit for Santa to wear. Draw a picture of Santa dressed in the new suit. Write a description of the suit.

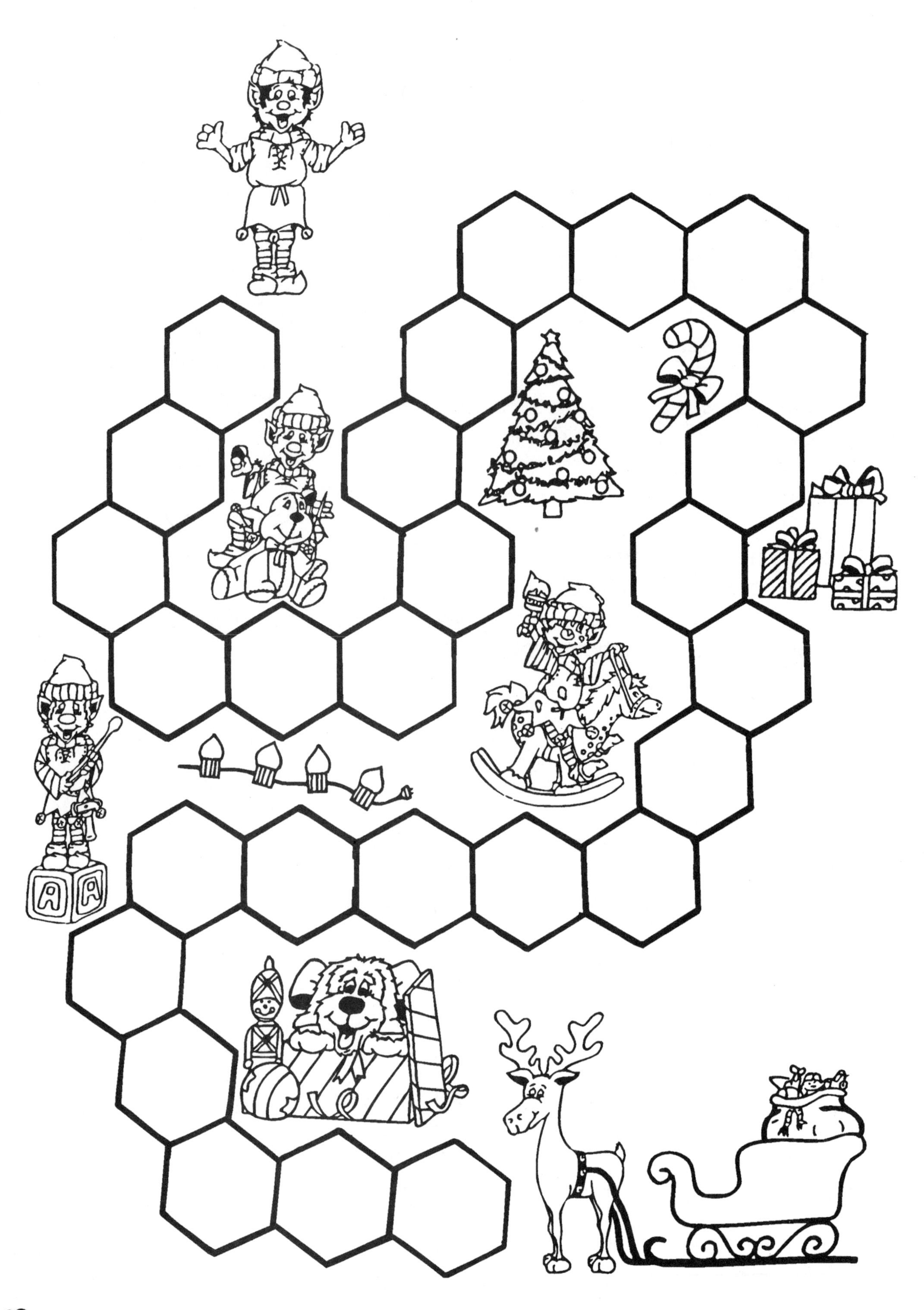

 When you were decorating the Christmas tree, you broke an ornament. Lose a turn.	 On, no! You got tangled up in the Christmas tree lights. Lose a turn.	 You ate too many candy canes. Now you have a stomachache! Go to bed. Lose a turn.
 While sewing your Christmas stocking, you ran out of thread. Go borrow some from Mrs. Claus. Go back 2 spaces.	 Oh, no! The Christmas puppy just jumped out of the box. Go back 1 space and find him!	 You need to feed the reindeer. Go ask Mrs. Claus for some carrots. Go ahead 2 spaces.
 The presents are all wrapped and ready to be loaded into the sleigh. Run ahead 3 spaces and put them in!	 Wow! You're ahead of schedule! Relax! Take a cookie and milk break! Move ahead 2 spaces.	 Br-r-r! It's cold at the North Pole. Santa needs his mittens. Run ahead 1 space and give them to him.

Name ____

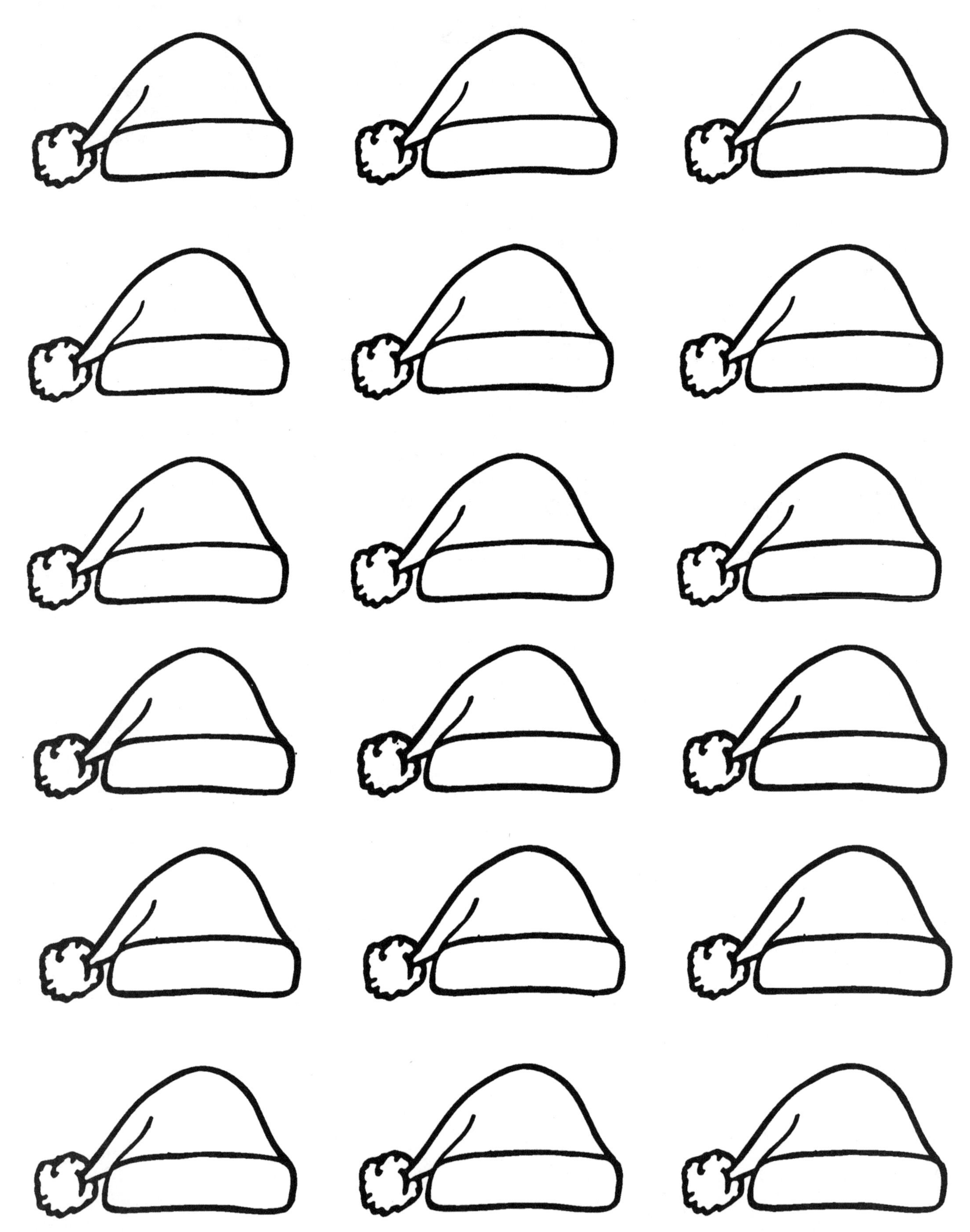

Name ___________________________________

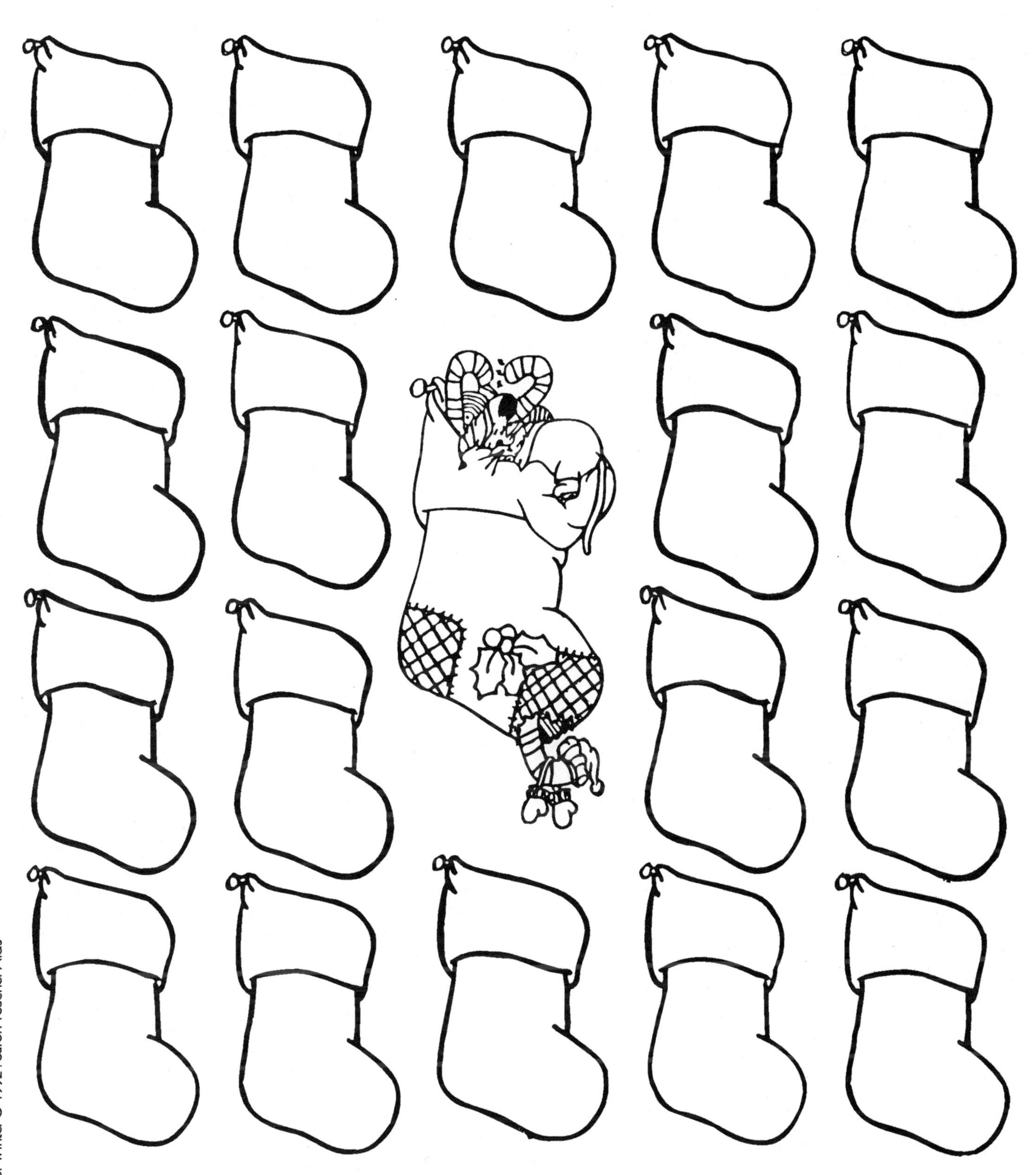

(child's name)

is at the top of Santa's list today because

(teacher's name)

Jingle! Jingle! Jingle!
All the way!

(child's name)

did very good work today!

(teacher's name)

JANUARY ACTIVITIES

January Activities

Name ______________________________

January

Sunday	Monday	Tuesday	Wednesday	Thursday	Friday	Saturday

CALENDAR ACTIVITIES

Print the following activities on squares of paper the same size as the spaces on the monthly calendar. Have the children cut out the following activity cards and then paste them on different calendar days.

Make a snowcone. Top it off with your favorite fruit juice.

Take an ice cube from the freezer. Predict how long it will take to melt.

Write a story about a snowman that would not melt.

How many snowflakes can you catch on your mitten?

Say something nice to a friend.

Make a "penguin cooler" with ice cream and 7-Up. Sprinkle coconut on top.

Do everything today wearing mittens.

Put colored water in a squeeze tube and write your name in the snow.

Getting Dressed

I dread winter, I really do,
'Cuz Mom makes such a big to-do
About getting dressed to go outside.
Sometimes I want to run and hide.

Of course, the thermal underwear comes first,
Then three sweaters and a shirt and
Some woolly socks that don't quite match.
I'm getting hot. I start to scratch.

Now I must put on my coat,
Then a warm scarf for my throat.
Mom has to wind it around my head
Until my face starts turning red.

Then my boots that weigh a ton.
Isn't this so much fun?
Mom says, "Wait! There's one thing more."
Oh, no! The earmuffs from my Aunt Lenore.

Mom smiles at me and makes a joke.
She says I'm cute. I almost choke.
But just between you and me,
It's nice to know she cares.

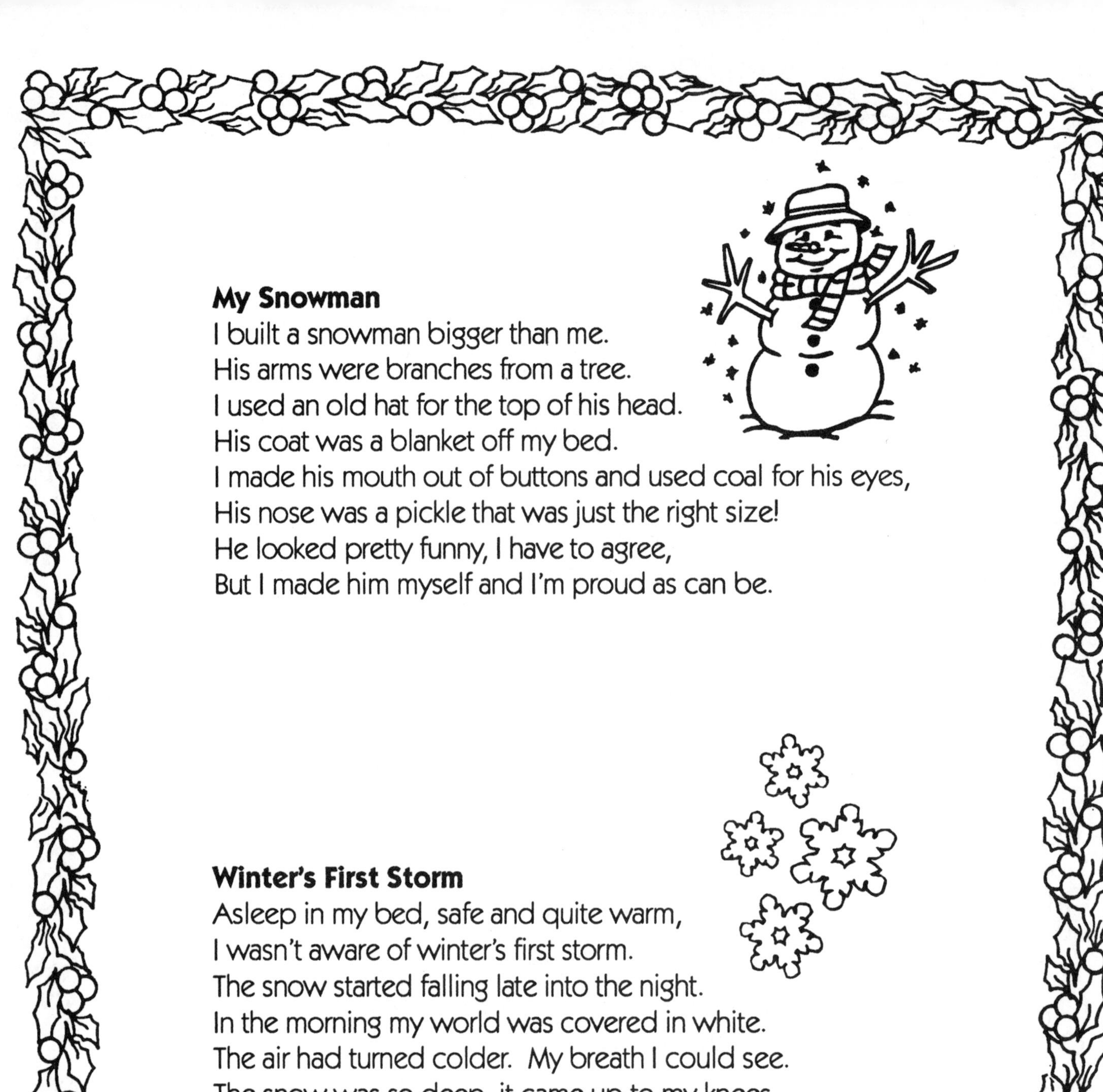

My Snowman
I built a snowman bigger than me.
His arms were branches from a tree.
I used an old hat for the top of his head.
His coat was a blanket off my bed.
I made his mouth out of buttons and used coal for his eyes,
His nose was a pickle that was just the right size!
He looked pretty funny, I have to agree,
But I made him myself and I'm proud as can be.

Winter's First Storm
Asleep in my bed, safe and quite warm,
I wasn't aware of winter's first storm.
The snow started falling late into the night.
In the morning my world was covered in white.
The air had turned colder. My breath I could see.
The snow was so deep, it came up to my knees.
Icicles hung from the limbs of the trees.
They looked like they'd fall with one little sneeze.
I thought I heard bells, but it was only the breeze
Blowing so gently through the ice-covered trees.
Then the sun hit my snow-covered world with its light,
And everything glistened. What a magical sight!
And to think this all happened
As I slept through the night!

A Lesson for Polo

Way up North where the cold winds blow,
The animals are used to the ice and the snow.

But the animals know that now and then,
A storm blows in that's even cold for them.

One of these storms was on its way,
And nobody knew how long it would stay.

Waddles, the penguin, and all of his friends
Started building igloos to protect all of them.

While Cecilia, the seal, and a walrus named Moe
Were out catching fish to store in the snow.

They all worked hard and as fast as they could.
Working together really felt good.

Only one animal wouldn't help out.
Polo, the polar bear, was just lying about.

Polo was lazy and mean as can be,
Always teasing and pushing every animal he'd see.

Polo did things just for spite,
Like knocking down igloos and starting a fight.

He threw a snowball and made Waddles cry
'Cuz the snowball he threw hit Waddles right in the eye.

When Polo saw Cecilia's fish on the ice,
He thought for his dinner the fish would be nice.

The storm was coming, but he didn't care.
They'd do his work for him 'cuz he was a mean, bully bear.

He was bigger and meaner, so no one would dare
Keep him out of their shelter. They'd just have to share.

One little penguin didn't think this was fair.
Everyone else was doing his or her share.

He said, "One at a time, Polo will bring us all down,
But standing together he can't boss us around!"

So they all went to Polo and told him they'd share
If he did his work. That would be fair.

Bullies are brave when it's just one-on-one,
But when faced with a group, they'll turn and run.

Polo just stood there, amazed as can be.
They weren't afraid. That he could see.

Polo gave in. What else could he do?
He pitched in and helped, wouldn't you?

QUESTIONS AND ACTIVITIES FOR THE STORY

1. Who were the main characters?
2. What were the animals getting ready for?
3. Where does this story take place?
4. How did the animals prepare for the storm? List the steps you follow to prepare for a storm.
5. Why did Polo finally decide to do his share of the work? Do you think Polo made the right decision?
6. Is working together and sharing ideas better than working all alone? Why? Why not? Think of all the different ways you can work together. Make a list.
7. Polo was surprised when the other animals stood up to him. Why? What did the animals learn by standing up to Polo?
8. Why do you think Polo was a bully? Give some examples.
9. Pretend you are Polo and explain why you think the other animals should do your work.
10. What good will come of Polo's helping out his animal friends? In what ways will Polo's help improve everyone's chances of surviving the storm?

Name ______________________________

Cut out the pictures below and paste them in the correct boxes.

My pet [ ] named Sam likes white fluffy [ ]. He follows me wherever I go. He rides behind me on my [ ] and wears my [ ] upon his head. For my [ ] arms, he fetches [ ], but chasing the [ ] is his best trick! I [ ] Sam as you can see. We're best friends—that Sam and me!

This booklet belongs to
(name)

This booklet belongs to
(name)

Name ______________________________

Name____

A mysterious-looking egg was left in Penelope Penguin's nest. It was too large for a penguin egg and definitely the wrong color. Nobody knows where it came from. Listen! There's a noise coming from inside the egg. Crack! Crack! What is it? Describe what has hatched from the mysterious egg. Draw a picture of it, too!

Attach to the top portion of your story.

Attach to the bottom portion of your story.

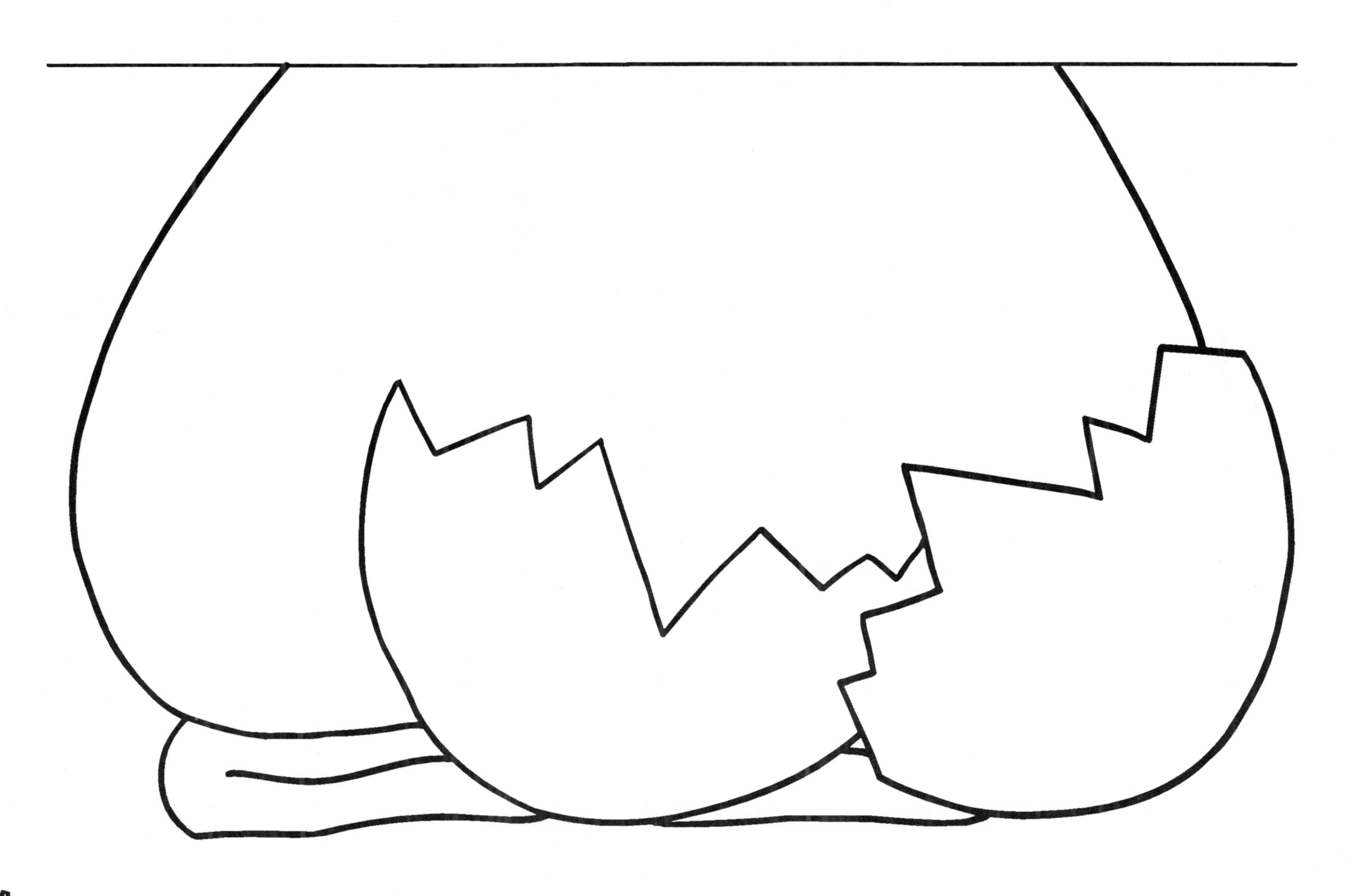

Name ____________________

Everybody thought it was pretty funny when Percy the penguin got stuck in the door of the igloo until. . . .
What happened to Percy the penguin?

Name ______________________________

If I had one million snowballs I would. . .

You love to skate. Move ahead 3 spaces.

Your stomach is growling. It must be time for lunch. You stop to go fishing. Lose a turn.

When you were sledding on the hill, you didn't wait for your turn. Lose a turn.

Br-r-r! Winter is cold. Go home and warm up. Drink some hot chocolate. Go back 2 spaces.

Crunch! Crunch! The snow is up to your knees. Go and get your snowshoes. Go back 3 spaces.

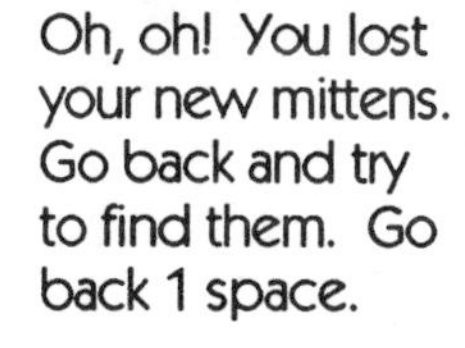

Oh, oh! You lost your new mittens. Go back and try to find them. Go back 1 space.

Whee! Sledding is a lot of fun! You went zooming down the hill. Move ahead 2 spaces.

You had a friendly snowball fight with a fish. Move ahead 3 spaces.

You're being chased by a polar bear. Quick! Hide in your igloo. Move ahead 1 space.

Name ___________________________________

Name ____

Name ______________________________

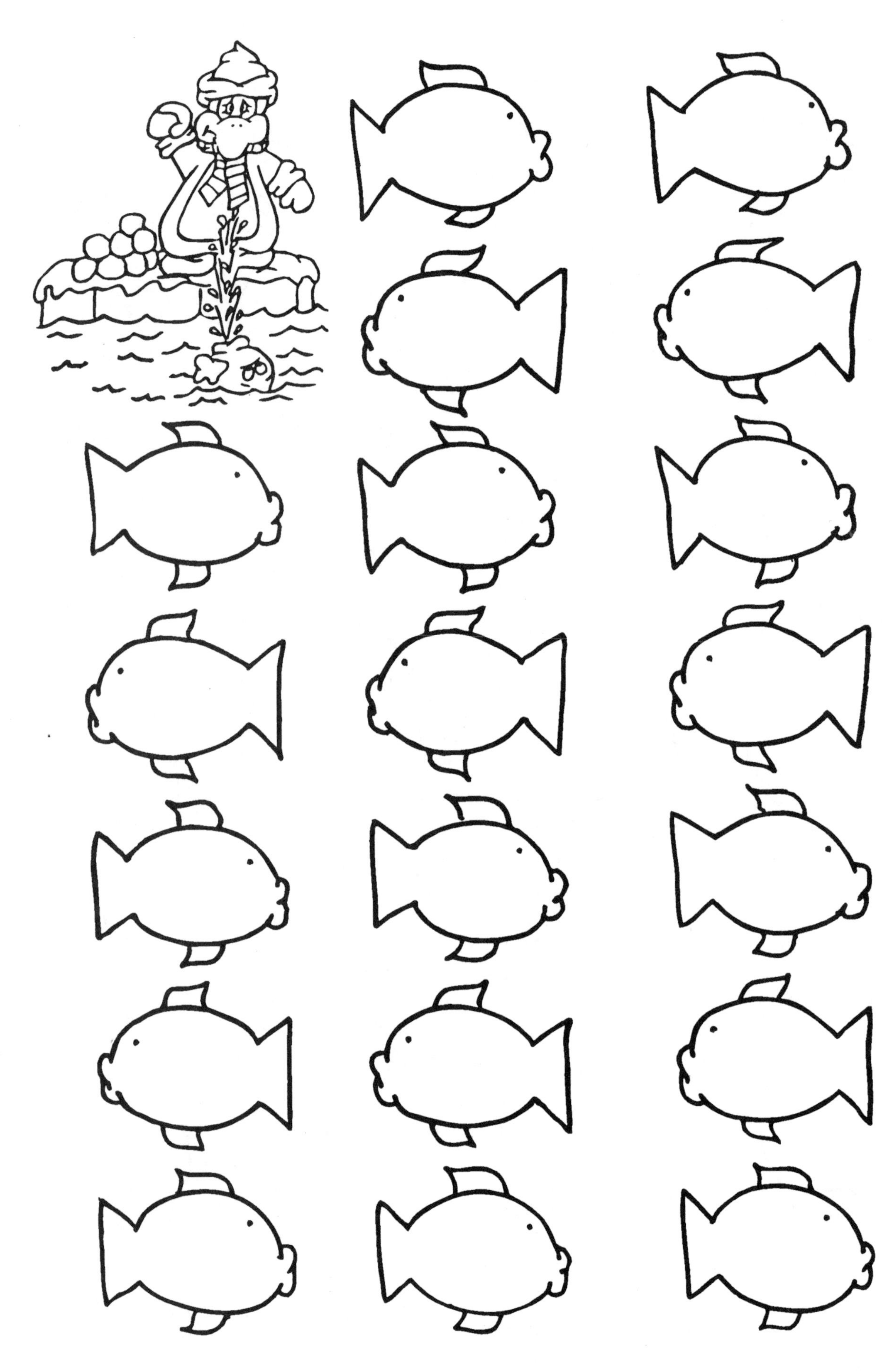

(child's name)

skated through work today!

(teacher's name)

Whee!

(child's name)

breezed through work today!

(teacher's name)

FEBRUARY ACTIVITIES

February Activities

Name ____

February

Sunday	Monday	Tuesday	Wednesday	Thursday	Friday	Saturday

CALENDAR ACTIVITIES

Print the following activities on squares of paper the same size as the spaces on the monthly calendar. Have the children cut out the following activity cards and then paste them on different calendar days.

Pretend you're a groundhog. Can you find your shadow? Measure it.

It's almost Valentine's Day. Start addressing your Valentines.

If Abe Lincoln were alive today, how old would he be?

Look at a five dollar bill and a one dollar bill. Which two Presidents are found on these bills?

Make a big red heart. Write "I Love You!" on it. Deliver it to a special friend.

Give someone you love a hug.

Say "Thanks!" to your parents for all that they do!

Help make and decorate some Valentine cookies.

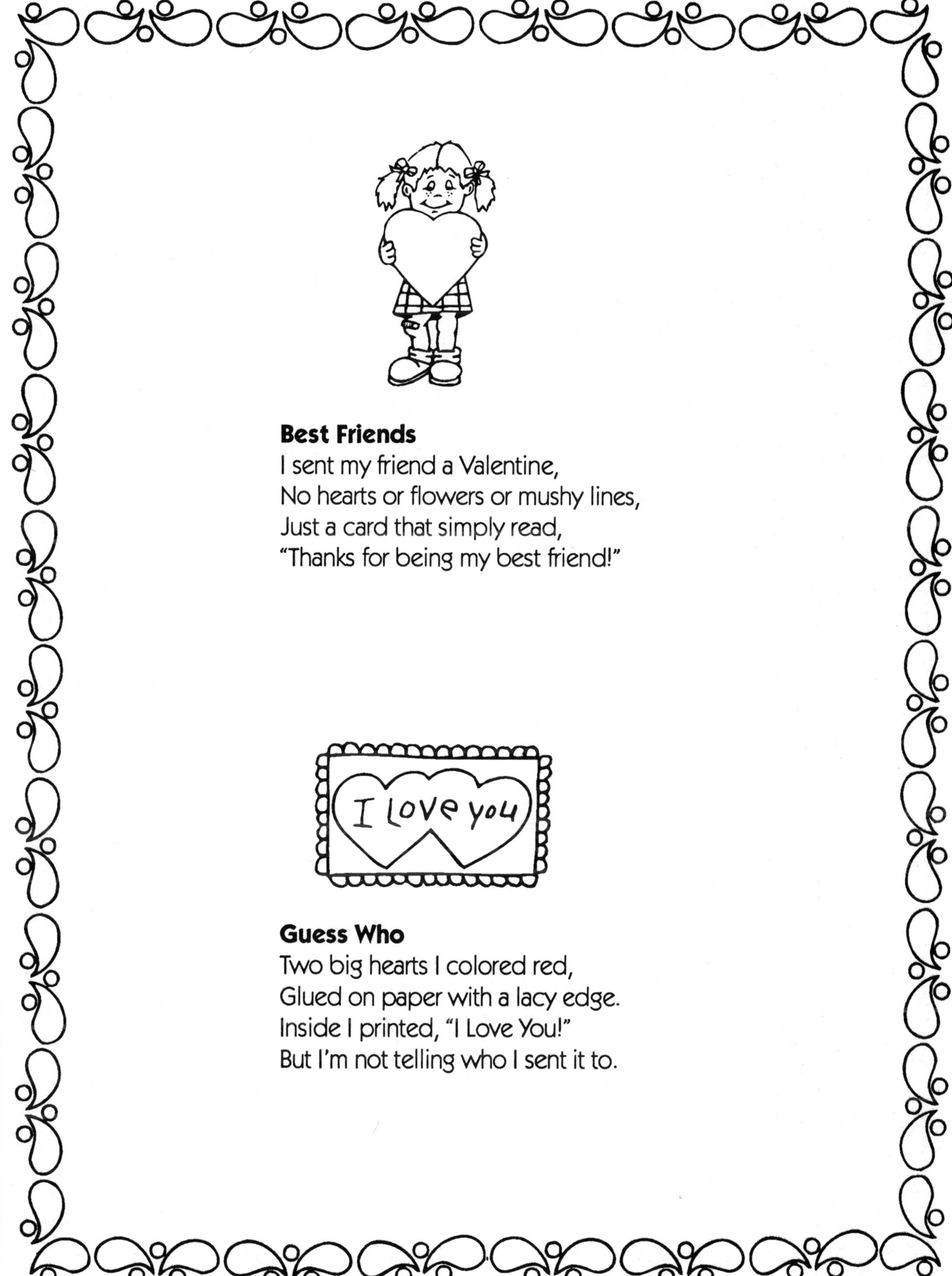

Best Friends

I sent my friend a Valentine,
No hearts or flowers or mushy lines,
Just a card that simply read,
"Thanks for being my best friend!"

Guess Who

Two big hearts I colored red,
Glued on paper with a lacy edge.
Inside I printed, "I Love You!"
But I'm not telling who I sent it to.

President's Day

It takes a very special person
To be the leader of our land,
To fight for what is right for all,
And never let our standards fall.
So we set aside a special day
To honor the Presidents of the U. S. A.

Mr. Groundhog's Shadow

A groundhog lives down deep in the ground.
He sleeps through the winter.
And every year about this time,
He wakes up and wonders,
"Is it time to get out of bed
Or pull the covers back over my head?"
So he pokes his head up out of the ground.
Will he see his shadow?

Feelings
This play is about some animal friends on Valentine's Day.

Cast:
Chipper the squirrel
Raymond the rabbit
Opal Lee the skunk
Hooter the owl (mail carrier)
Other forest animals

Props:
Mail bag
Valentines

Scene 1

Scene 1 opens with Chipper very busily making Valentine's Day cards for his friends, Raymond and Opal Lee.

Chipper: Acorns are tan.
Chestnuts are brown.
If I smelled like you,
I'd keep perfume around!

Perfect for Opal Lee! She's really going to laugh at that Valentine's Day message. She'll know it's only a joke. Hm-m-m. Now let's see, for my best friend Raymond . . .

The leaves are green.
The trees are brown.
Raymond's teeth
Are the biggest around.

I can hardly wait to see Raymond's face when he reads his Valentine's Day message.

Scene 1 ends with Chipper laughing and mailing his so-called humorous Valentines to his friends.

Scene 2

Scene 2 opens deep in the forest. All the animals are gathered together for a Valentine's Day celebration. Hooter, the mail carrier, arrives and delivers Valentines to the animals.

Hooter: Chipper! Chipper! I have a couple of Valentines for you. Opal Lee! Raymond! Here are a few Valentines for you, too. (Hooter moves off to deliver Valentines to the other forest animals. After all the Valentines have been delivered, the animals take turns reading their Valentines out loud.)

Opal Lee: Chipper, you go first. Share a Valentine with us!

Chipper: Okay. (He opens his first Valentine and reads it.)
Flowers are pretty
And smell so sweet.
To have friends like you
Sure is neat! Signed Opal Lee.

Animals: Oh! Ah! That's so nice. (Chipper is beginning to look a little uncomfortable.)

Raymond: Read mine next, Chipper. It's great!

Chipper: Carrots are orange.
Cabbage is green.
You're the best friend
I've ever seen. Signed Raymond.

Animals: Oh! Ah! (Chipper is beginning to question his humorous Valentines. Maybe he shouldn't have been so thoughtless. It might have been better just to write about how he really feels towards his friends instead of turning it into a joke!)

Opal Lee: I'll go next. I think I'll read Chipper's Valentine to me first. (Chipper starts to look really nervous and squirms.)
Acorns are tan.
Chestnuts are brown.
If I smelled like you,
I'd keep perfume around! Signed Chipper.

Animals: (Gasp!) Oh! No! Poor Opal Lee. How embarrassing. Chipper, how could you?

Opal Lee: (Opal Lee starts to cry and runs off into the forest.) Sniff! Sniff! Chipper, how could you?

Raymond: (Says very suspiciously!) Maybe I should go next.
The leaves are green.
The trees are brown.
Raymond's teeth
Are the biggest around! Signed Chipper.

Animals: (Gasp!) Oh, no! Chipper, what a terrible thing to say—especially to a friend.

Raymond: (Embarrassed and hurt!) Chipper, I thought you were my friend. How could you hurt Opal Lee's and my feelings like this? (Raymond runs off into the forest to find Opal Lee.)

Chipper: What's the matter? Can't you take a joke?

Scene 2 ends with Chipper walking all alone back to his home.

Scene 3

Scene 3 opens with Chipper at home busily making new Valentines for his two friends. On the way home, he had time to think about Valentine's Day. He realized that Valentine's Day is the one day out of the year to tell your friends how you really feel about them.

Chipper: I hope these new Valentine's Day cards will let Raymond and Opal Lee know exactly how I feel about them. I hope they'll understand that I really didn't mean to hurt their feelings.

Scene 3 ends with Chipper walking into the forest to find his two friends and deliver his new Valentines.

Scene 4

Scene 4 opens with Chipper finding his two friends, Raymond and Opal Lee, splashing their feet in the river.

Chipper: Hi! I'm glad I found you. (Raymond and Opal Lee ignore Chipper and continue to talk between themselves.) I'm so sorry! I didn't mean to hurt your feelings. It was only supposed to be a joke.

Opal Lee: Chipper, you might have thought it was funny, but I was so embarrassed.

Raymond: I know I have big teeth, Chipper, but sometimes people are very sensitive about how they look.

Chipper: I guess it's okay to tease people and tell jokes, but I should try to be a little more considerate and sensitive about your feelings, especially on Valentine's Day. All kidding aside, this is how I really feel! (Chipper hands the new Valentine's Day cards to his friends.)

Raymond: Leaves are green.
Trees are brown.
Friends like you
Aren't easily found. Signed Chipper.
Gee, Chipper, that's really nice. Thank you!

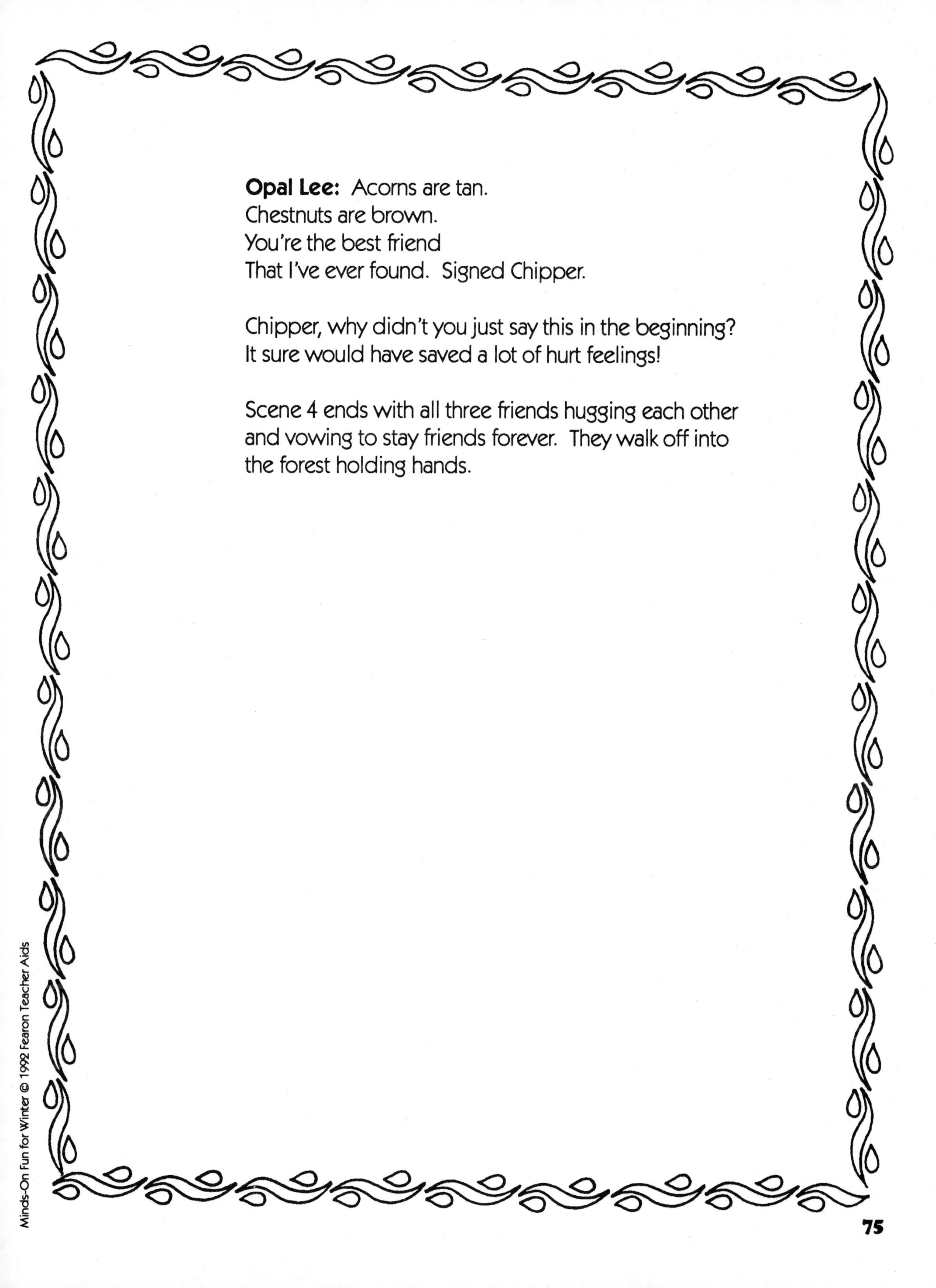

Opal Lee: Acorns are tan.
Chestnuts are brown.
You're the best friend
That I've ever found. Signed Chipper.

Chipper, why didn't you just say this in the beginning?
It sure would have saved a lot of hurt feelings!

Scene 4 ends with all three friends hugging each other and vowing to stay friends forever. They walk off into the forest holding hands.

QUESTIONS AND ACTIVITIES FOR THE PLAY

1. Who was the main character in this story?
2. What were the animals exchanging with one another? What events caused Chipper to make new Valentines for his friends?
3. Why were the animals having a party?
4. In your own words, tell what happened first, second, third, and so on.
5. What is this story all about?
6. Have you ever hurt a friend's feelings? Have your feelings ever been hurt by a friend? Why is it good to talk about hurt feelings?
7. Why do you think Chipper made a joke out of the Valentines instead of telling his friends how he really felt about them? Is making jokes about people ever a nice thing to do? Why or why not?
8. Chipper made new Valentines for his friends. How did this help to solve the problem of hurt feelings? What other ways might Chipper have used to show his friends he was sorry for hurting their feelings? Make a list.
9. Why do friends sometimes tease one another? What are some of the consequences of teasing friends?
10. What could you do to make a friend feel better?

Name ____

Cut out the pictures below and paste them in the correct boxes.

I made my pets a Valentine, a big red [ ] that said, "Be Mine!" The first one went to a [ ] purring on my lap. The second one went to my [ ] named Spot. He buried it in the back! The third one went to a [ ] that lives inside his shell. The fourth one went to a pretty [ ] that doesn't sing so well. The fifth one went to a [ ] that lives up in a [ ]. The sixth one went to a [ ] that always comforts me. The last one went to my pet [ ]. I found him running around my [ ].

turtle	cat	dog	bird	heart

house	tree	bear	squirrel	mouse

This booklet belongs to
(name)

This booklet belongs to
(name)

Name ______________________________

Name ______________________________

Imagine that while exploring planet Ziblon, a Ziblonian gave you a very special Valentine. Invent a Ziblonian alphabet. Then write a Valentine message using your new alphabet. Use your imagination. Decode and translate the Valentine message as well.

Attach to the top portion of your message.

Attach to the bottom portion of your message.

Name ______________________________

Do you ever wonder who writes the Valentine messages on all those little candy hearts? Pretend you work in a Valentine candy heart factory and it is your job to write the messages. Make up some new and creative Valentine messages to print on the hearts provided below.

Name ____________________

Friends are very special.
That's why there is a day
To show them how you feel inside
In a lot of little ways.

Make up a very special Valentine's Day message for one of your friends.

Name ______________________________

Mr. Horace T. Groundhog invited me
To visit his den for some cinnamon tea.
He wrote out directions and gave me a map.
He said, "Wear a sweater. The tunnels are damp."
I needed a light. It was dark as can be.
I even passed under the roots of a tree.
It was a long, winding tunnel, but at the end was his door.
We drank tea and ate cookies and talked until four!

Write out the directions to Mr. Horace T. Groundhog's den.
Make a map, too.

Name ______________________________

Would you like to be President of the United States?

1. Are you a citizen of the United States?
2. Are you 35 years or older?
3. Have you lived in the United States for 14 years?

Pretend you are President of the United States. Draw a picture of yourself as President. Remember, you must be at least 35 years old. What would you do if you were President?

____

____

____

____

____

____

Name ____________________

Bart loves Daisy and Daisy loves Bart.
But telling each other was very hard.
You see, they were dragons, so with each
word they spoke,
Out came an inferno of fire and smoke.
I guess you could say their love was "aflame,"
And so was Daisy when Bart spoke her name!

Use your imagination. Write a smoke-puff message to Daisy from Bart. Translate the smoke-puff message here.

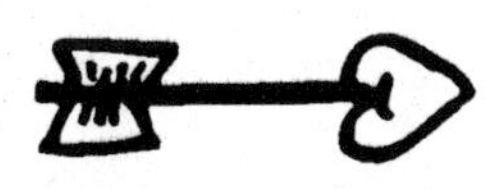 You lost your Cupid arrow. Go back 2 spaces and try to find it.	 Bong! You missed your target. Go back 1 space and try again. Good luck!	You bought your mother a big box of chocolates for Valentine's Day, but you ate the entire box. Go back 3 spaces and buy her another box. 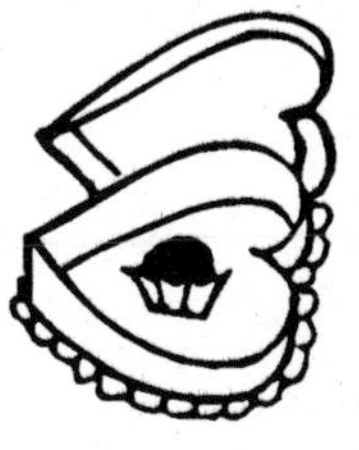
 Stinky the skunk stopped to pick some petunias for his girlfriend. Lose a turn.	Darwin the dragon accidently breathed on his Valentines and burned them up. Lose a turn. 	Oh, no! You forgot your Valentines. Go home and get them. Lose a turn.  
Hurry to deliver a singing Valentine to Mr. and Mrs. Lovebird. Go ahead 2 spaces. 	 Roses are red, violets are blue. I made a Valentine just for you. Go ahead 3 spaces.	 You made a very special Valentine for your parents. Go ahead 1 space. 

Name ____

Name ____

(child's name)

aimed high and achieved a goal today!

(teacher's name)

(child's name)

scooted through work today!

(teacher's name)

Be
My
Valentine